The Glass Painting

Projects and artwork by Cheryl Owen
Photography by Stillview Photography
Written by Lisa Telford

Licensed exclusively to Top That Publishing Ltd
Tide Mill Way, Woodbridge, Suffolk, IP12 1AP, UK
www.topthatpublishing.com
Copyright © 2014 Tide Mill Media
Printed and bound in China

BK54210

Contents

An Introduction to Glass Painting

Getting Started

The art of glass painting has historical roots,
with many astounding pieces on view in religious
buildings and ancient houses around the world.
It is comparatively easy to recreate these
wonderful works of art in your own home,
or to give glass items a modern twist using
the same techniques. All you need are
an eye for beautiful designs, a steady hand,
and the patience to practise the techniques
before attempting your own masterpiece!

Equipment for Glass Painting

Before You Start

You may be wondering where to start with this seemingly complex hobby – but don't panic! The basic kit you need can be purchased from craft and hobby shops and is relatively inexpensive. There are also specialist websites on the internet that are easy to find.

Glass Paints

The most basic items you will need are, fairly obviously, glass paints. Colours can be mixed from the three primary colours (see page 8) but some colours are better purchased ready-mixed. Shop-bought paints offer a wide variety of vibrant colours and allow you to choose exactly the right shade.

Outliner

The basic black outliner used in many projects is a must-have. It is used to keep the paints within a specific area of your work, although some projects avoid this for a different effect. Other colours of outliner can also be bought, and metallic colours add an extra dimension to your work. They can be added on top of the paint when it is dry for an additional paint effect.

Paint Surfaces

Glass paints can be used on a variety of surfaces. In addition to glass, they can be painted on to clear plastic, and acetate sheets (which can be bought in different thicknesses and sizes from craft shops). If possible, test the paints on your surface to ensure that the surface will not corrode.

Painting Tool

Small paintbrushes are suitable for painting on to glass, but specialis tools are also available. They are easier to use and easier to clean between colours. Read page 6 to find out how to use these tools to their best effect, and practise before attempting a project to get used to the feel of a painting tool and how it applies the paint.

Cleaning Up

As with most crafts, you should cover your clothes and your work surface before you begin, to avoid unnecessary cleaning up. Spilt paint can be removed from work surfaces with kitchen towel and a small amount of methylated spirit; wipe up any excess and dab the stain before it dries. Keep the rim of your paint pots clean to prevent the lids sticking when they are stored.

Basic Techniques

Practise First

Like all new skills, you should expect to have some poor attempts before you produce anything of quality. Collect old glass jars to practise on, or buy inexpensive acetate stationery items which can still be used if your first designs leave something to be desired!

Applying the Paint

Dip your brush or tool into the paint and dot it on to your glass surface. Practise spreading the paint across small areas without leaving 'brush strokes' behind. Make sure that you have enough paint to fill the desired area; too little paint will leave more visible strokes.

Larger Areas

To fill larger areas of colour, use the blunt end of a painting tool if you have one. Again, make sure that you keep adding more paint as required to fill the space. Whenever possible, try to support your work so that you are painting on to a horizontal surface. This will prevent any colour flooding to the bottom of the outlined area.

A Neat Finish

When the colour fills the majority of the outlined space, use a fine brush or the pointed end of a painting tool to push the colour right into the corners and edges of the area. If you have too much colour, lift some off with the tool, or use a cotton bud to remove excess paint.

Changing Colour

Always clean your brush or painting tool before using it to apply a different colour. Whenever possible, allow areas of one colour to dry before starting work with the next colour. Some projects use two colours merging into one another, and this should be done while the first colour is still wet.

Techniques

Always start to paint in the centre of a design, and work outwards as each colour dries. Where colours merge, use a cocktail stick or the clean point of a tool to drag the colours into each other slightly. Some projects suggest applying a darker shade just outside your basic colour for a shadow effect.

Colour Wheel

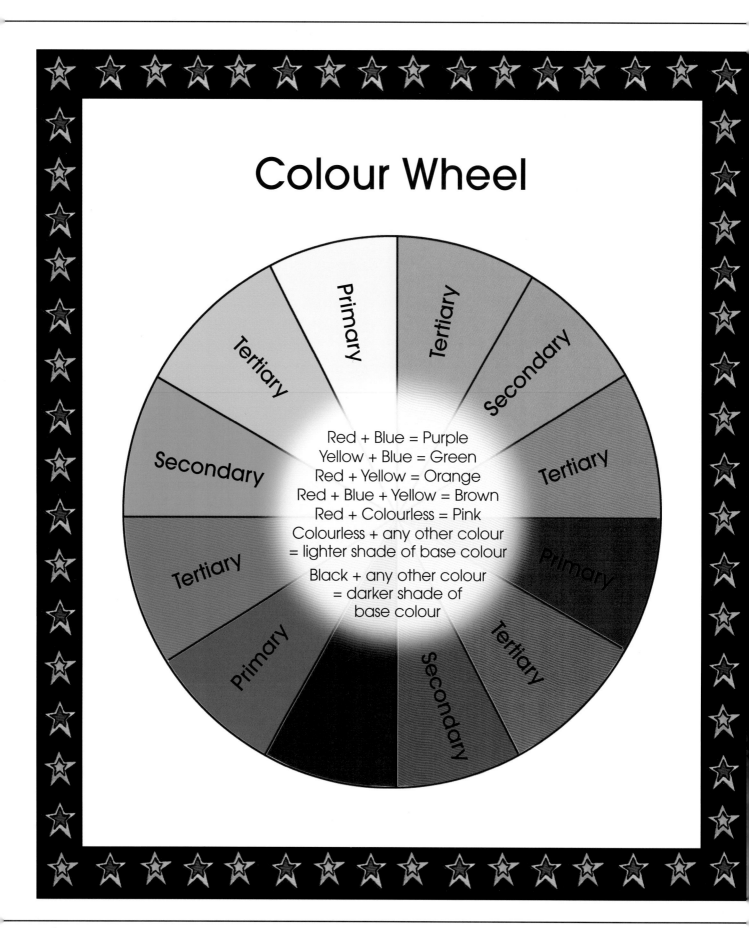

Primary

Tertiary

Secondary

Tertiary

Tertiary

Secondary

Primary

Tertiary

Primary

Secondary

Red + Blue = Purple
Yellow + Blue = Green
Red + Yellow = Orange
Red + Blue + Yellow = Brown
Red + Colourless = Pink
Colourless + any other colour
= lighter shade of base colour

Black + any other colour
= darker shade of
base colour

Mixing Colours

Paint Palette

The basic colour rules of paints also apply to glass paints: mix blue and yellow to create green, red and yellow to create orange, and blue and red to create purple. Experiment with smaller or larger amounts of each to obtain different shades and strengths of colour. The colour wheel opposite allows you to see easily the different shades available from the three primary colours.

Pastel Shade

To obtain paler shades of the three primary colours, and of the secondary colours mixed from them, you will have to add a colourless glass paint. This can be bought from hobby shops and craft shops, and simply lightens any other colour when mixed together.

Ready-mixed Colour

You will find as you mix your paints that some colours are more easily achieved than others. Certain colours will appear slightly 'muddy', and it is easier to buy the exact shade you require to avoid this muddiness. Remember also that it is difficult to mix exactly the same shade twice; if you plan to paint an item over several days, or have large areas to fill with the same colour, mixing your own paint could cause problems. A ready-mixed colour will allow you to stop and start at your leisure without the worry of re-mixing the colour to match.

Green

Orange

Purple

Applying Outliner

Using the Outliner Pen

An outliner pen has a pointed nozzle to direct the paint in a fine, precise line. However, the hardest part of glass painting is to create a smooth, even outline without bubbles or blotches. Practise applying the outliner in one flowing movement – it really is harder than you might imagine!

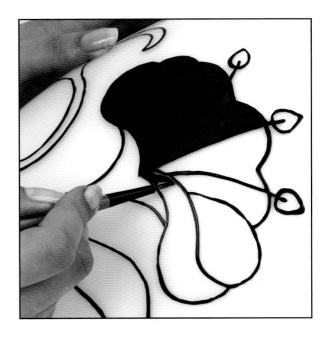

Outlining Your Design

Most of the projects in this book use templates, which are all supplied at the back (see page 58). Trace off the desired pattern and follow the instructions to position the template correctly. Once in place, you can simply follow the pattern with your outliner pen. Leave this to dry thoroughly before you start to apply coloured paint.

The Finished Product

Many items you paint will be purely for decoration, but you should bear in mind what the item's use will be before you paint it. You should always paint the underside of any bowl or jug you may want to place food or drink in – never place food directly onto a glass-painted surface. Water-based glass paints can only be gently wiped clean, and never immersed in water for washing.

Solvent-based paints are more durable, but painted items should still be washed gently and carefully, and never in a dishwasher.

Quick & Easy Projects

One of the most difficult parts of glass painting is successfully applying the paint without leaving streaks and patchy areas. Use these simple starter projects to perfect your technique before moving on to anything more ambitious.

Sun Catchers

A sun catcher is a glass or plastic shape which is painted
and hung to catch the light. Sun catchers are available from hobby stores
and are a great way to start glass painting.

YOU WILL NEED:
- *Red, yellow and blue glass paints*
- *Painting tool or brush*
- *Three plastic sun catcher shapes (we have used a fish in the steps below)*

Step 1

Lay your sun catchers on your work area with the textured side of the ridged areas facing downwards. If you have chosen a fish, start with this. Use the pointed end of your painting tool to apply blue paint to the fish's eye, the stripe across the eye, and alternate stripes thereafter.

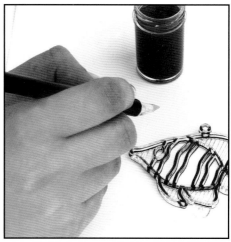

Step 1

Step 2

Now paint in the remaining stripes, using red paint. Remember, it is easiest to start at the centre of a piece and work outwards. Push the paint into the very edges of the area, turning the sun catcher to ensure that no areas remain unpainted. Paint the fins using red paint, still working on the unridged side.

Step 2

Step 3

Finally, paint the head of the fish using yellow paint, and leave to dry. Paint the other sun catchers in the same way, working from the centre outwards and applying paint to the unridged side of the plastic. Be especially careful to apply enough paint to any large surface areas (like the starfish pictured) to avoid a patchy effect when held up to the light.

Step 3

Clip Frame Decoration

YOU WILL NEED:
- *Glass clip frame*
- *1.2 cm wide masking tape*
- *Yellow and red glass paints*
- *Painting tool or brush*
- *Kitchen towel*
- *Cotton bud and methylated spirit*

Step 1

Remove the clips and lift the glass off the frame. Use masking tape to make a border around all four edges of the glass. Mask off a 3 cm square in each corner. Stick strips of masking tape 2 cm inside the outer tapes between the squares. Press the edges of the masking tape firmly to prevent paint from bleeding underneath.

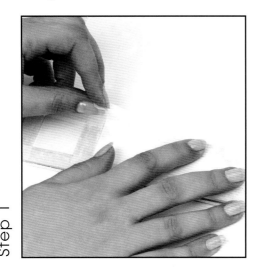

Step 1

Step 2

Paint each of the rectangles forming the border using a rich yellow colour. Use a brush or the blunt end of a painting tool, generously loaded with paint. Allow this colour to dry. Mix a rich orange colour to use in the corners.

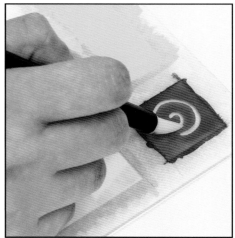

Step 2

Paint one corner square in rich orange. Then, using the end of a paintbrush or the pointed end of a painting tool, draw a spiral in the wet paint. Wipe off the excess paint on kitchen towel.

Step 3

Step 3

Repeat this last process in each corner square, drawing a spiral in each whilst still wet. Leave to dry overnight. When the paint is completely dry, carefully peel off the masking tape. If necessary, neaten any edges with a cotton bud dipped in methylated spirit.

Key Fobs

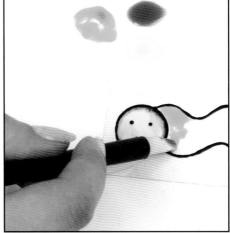

YOU WILL NEED:
- *Tracing paper*
- *Soft pencil*
- *Acetate sheets*
- *Black outliner pen*
- *Scissors*
- *Glass paints*
- *Painting tool or brush*
- *Pin or needle*
- *Key ring*

Step 1
Trace the templates of the caterpillar, bee and ladybird from pages 58 and 61. Tape the templates underneath a sheet of thick acetate and draw around each outline with black outliner. Allow the outliner to dry.

Step 2
Paint the black areas of the ladybird and the bee and leave them to dry thoroughly. Paint the ladybird's red back sections and dot in blue eyes. Paint the yellow stripes on the bee and paint the face in yellow as well.

Step 3A
Mix together blue and yellow to make a green. Paint the body of the caterpillar with blue and green stripes, allowing the two colours to bleed together. Mix a little more blue into the green to make turquoise and apply around the edge of the caterpillar's face.

Step 3B
Use this colour to paint along the top edges of the bee's wings.

Step 4
Fill the centre of the bee's wings and the caterpillar's face with colourless paint. When all the paints are dry, cut out each shape. Pierce a hole in each and attach to metal key fobs.

Step 3A

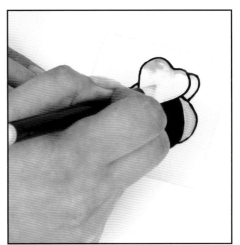

Step 3B

Step 4

Nursery Mobile

YOU WILL NEED:
- *Tracing paper*
- *Soft pencil*
- *Acetate sheets*
- *Black outliner pen*
- *Red, yellow and blue glass paints*
- *Colourless paint*
- *Painting tool or brush*
- *Scissors*
- *Mobile wires*
- *Cotton thread*
- *Superglue*

Step 1

Trace the sheep template from page 58, using a soft pencil and tracing paper. Tape this outline underneath a sheet of thick acetate. Carefully draw around the sheep using the black outliner pen, omitting the cross. Repeat this to draw four sheep in total.

Step 2

Mix four pastel shades of paint: lilac, blue, pink and orange. Use a different colour for the hooves of each of the four sheep. Add colourless paint to each of the pastels, to make a lighter shade of each. Paint the wool with these new shades, matching each to the colour of the hooves.

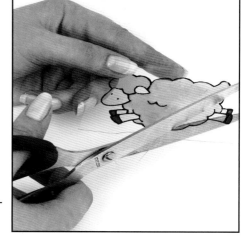

Step 3

Add more colourless paint to lighten the colours further. Use these new colours to paint the legs, ears and face of each sheep. When all the paints are dry, carefully cut out.

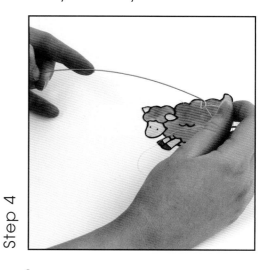

Step 4

To assemble the mobile, pierce a hole in each sheep where the cross is marked on the template, and tie thread through each hole. Tie the other end of each thread to your mobile wires. Cross the wires at the centre and tie together. Dab the intersection with superglue to secure.

Handmade Butterfly Cards

YOU WILL NEED:
- *Tracing paper*
- *Soft pencil*
- *Acetate sheets*
- *Black outliner pen*
- *Scissors*
- *Glass paints*
- *Painting tool*
- *Three-fold window card with 8.2cm circular hole*
- *White paper*
- *Spray adhesive*
- *Double-sided tape*

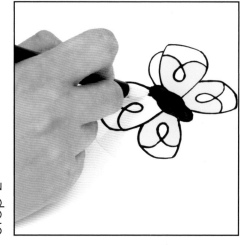

Step 2

Step 1
Trace the butterfly template from page 61 and tape the template under a sheet of acetate. Draw the outline using black outliner, and leave to dry. Cut around the dotted lines of the template.

Step 2
Paint the butterfly in your chosen colours, starting from the centre and working outwards. Use the blunt end of a painting tool for larger, solid areas such as the body, ensuring that the paint coverage is even.

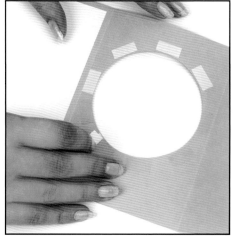

Step 3A

Step 3A
Open the card and lay it with the left side facing upwards. Cut a piece of white paper which measures 5 mm less on all sides than the card front. Use spray adhesive to attach the paper to the left-hand flap of the card. Place double-sided tape around the edge of the circle.

Step 3B
Stick the acetate under the hole using double-sided tape. Attach the flap underneath the front of the card, using double-sided tape around the edges.

Step 3B

Tea Light Holders

YOU WILL NEED:
- *Tracing paper*
- *Soft pencil*
- *Scissors*
- *Tea light holder*
- *Masking tape*
- *Black outliner pen*
- *Blue, red and yellow glass paints*
- *Painting tool*
- *Modelling clay*

Step 1

Trace the flower template from page 58. Cut along the dotted lines, and position the tracing paper inside the tea light holder. Hold in place with masking tape. Carefully draw along the outlines with black outliner, keeping the line as fine as possible. When the first pattern is dry, turn the tea light and repeat, until you have outlines surrounding the tea light on all sides.

Step 1

Step 2

Paint each of the flowers in a simple primary colour. Allow the flowers to dry before you turn the holder to continue, to avoid smudging the paint. Support the tea light holder between two small pieces of modelling clay or sticky putty to keep it in position.

Step 2

Step 3

Mix yellow and blue to create green for the leaves, and paint these on each flower. You could paint all the leaves at once, keeping the tea light holder vertical and turning it, but make sure that the paint doesn't run to the bottom of the leaf shapes.

Step 3

Herb Jars

YOU WILL NEED:
- *Small glass jars with lids*
- *Blue, red, yellow and colourless glass paints*
- *Painting tool or brush*

Step 1

Mix two shades of green paint using a combination of blue, yellow and colourless paint. Paint the stems using careful freehand strokes with the pointed end of a painting tool or a fine brush. Add short outward stokes to the rosemary stems. Paint leaves on the thyme stems. Leave them to dry.

Step 2

Add the flowers to the stems of each of the different herbs. Use pinpricks of blue for the rosemary flowers, carefully dotting small amounts of paint in clusters up each stem.

Step 3

Mix a bright magenta pink for the flowers of the chives. Form small dots of petals for each flower. Add colourless paint to this pink to make a paler pink for the thyme. Form the main flowers at the top of each stem with a cluster of dots, and add single dots further down the stems.

Advanced Projects

As your confidence builds, it is satisfying to
display your talents on larger, more complex
projects which can be displayed in more
prominent places in your home.
Where possible, paint on to a horizontal surface
before mounting your work on a wall or door,
to prevent the paint running down
to the bottom of the painting area.

Mirror Plaque 1

YOU WILL NEED:
- *Mirror tile (15 cm square)*
- *Silver and gold outliner pens*
- *Glass nuggets*
- *Chinagraph pencil*

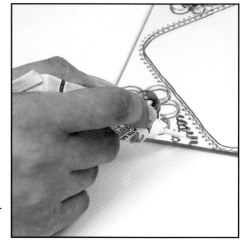
Step 3

Step 1

Using the template from page 63, copy the design on to your mirror tile using a chinagraph pencil. Draw the central diamond using the silver outliner pen. Use strong glue to fix a glass nugget in each corner of the tile, and leave them to dry.

Step 2

Draw in the flowers using gold outliner. Leave a margin of at least 2 mm between the petals and the silver diamond.

Step 3

Add gold dots around the main silver diamond shape in the centre. Draw a line of dots just inside the silver diamond, and another just outside. Leave this to dry, then decorate the remaining space in each corner using the silver outliner pen. Use freehand squirls and squiggles, keeping the lines fine and neat.

Step 2

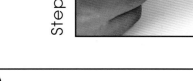

— Mirror Plaque 2 —

YOU WILL NEED:
- *Mirror tile (15cm square)*
- *Black outliner pen*
- *Blue, red and yellow glass paints*
- *Painting tool or brush*
- *Tracing paper*

Step 1

Cut out a 7 cm square of tracing paper. Tape the square to the centre of your mirror tile and with black outliner draw around it. Leave to dry, then carefully remove the paper.

Step 1

NOTE: When painting the plaque, remember the basic technique: start from the centre and work out towards the edges. Push the colour into every corner of each shape. Don't skimp on paint or the end result will be patchy and uneven. Paint the plaque in quarters, leaving each section to dry before starting the next.

Step 2

Draw mosaic shapes, freehand, around the square. Run a line of outliner along each outer edge of the tile. It may be worth sketching a rough mosaic design on to paper first, to ensure that you're happy with the final shapes. Leave the tile to dry.

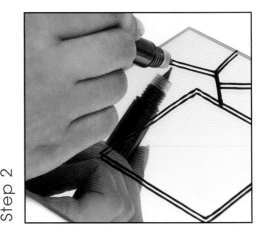

Step 2

Step 3

Paint each of the sections a different colour. Again, practise your scheme first, so that you don't end up with two adjacent sections of the same colour. The finished plaque should have a balance of colour overall.

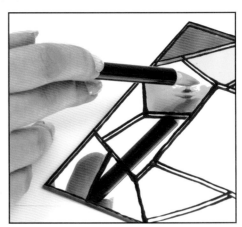

Step 3

Anniversary Bowl

YOU WILL NEED:
- *Tracing paper*
- *Soft pencil*
- *Scissors*
- *Shallow, wide-rimmed glass bowl*
- *Masking tape*
- *Silver outliner pen*
- *Blue, red and yellow glass paints*
- *Painting tool or brush*

Step 1

Step 1

Trace the flower and leaf templates from pages 34 and 62 on to tracing paper. Carefully draw the initials of your choice, (from page 62), on to the tracing paper.

Step 2

Cut out the templates and position them under the rim of the bowl using small pieces of masking tape to secure them. Place the crossed leaves between the initials with the single leaves at each side. Ensure that the flowers are evenly spaced around the rest of the bowl, with varying numbers of leaves.

Step 2

Step 3

Very carefully, draw along the outline of each shape with silver outliner. Keep the lines as fine and delicate as possible, using a flowing movement for the spirals of each flower. Leave the outliner to dry, overnight if possible.

Step 3

Step 4

Mix the paint for the roses using a large amount of red with a small dab of yellow, until you achieve the colour you desire. Carefully paint in each of the flowers.

Step 5

Add more yellow to the colour of the flowers, and use this new colour to paint in each of the initials. Leave these colours to dry.

Step 6

Finally, mix blue and yellow to make green for the leaves. Paint each of the leaves, working around the bowl, being careful not to smudge the previous paint as you turn the bowl around.

Templates

Step 4

Step 5

Step 6

Spotted Vase

YOU WILL NEED:
- *Circular stickers in two sizes*
- *Glass vase*
- *Ceramic tile or old plate*
- *Natural sponge*
- *Glass paints – colours of your choice*

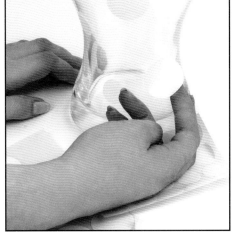

Step 1

Step 2

Step 3

Step 1

Stick the stickers to the vase to create a random pattern of spots. Make sure that the edges are pressed down firmly to prevent paint bleeding underneath when it is applied.

Step 2

Mix your chosen colour of paint on the tile or old plate. Use the sponge to dab at the paint and then apply the paint to the vase. You should be able to work around the whole vase in one session, as the paint is not applied liberally enough to run. Experiment with holding the vase upside down on one hand to apply the paint all over.

Step 3

When the paint is completely dry, remove the stickers to reveal the pattern of spots.

Celtic Carafe & Glasses

YOU WILL NEED:
- *Tracing paper*
- *Soft pencil*
- *Scissors*
- *Water carafe and glasses*
- *Masking tape*
- *Chinagraph pencil*
- *Gold outliner pen*
- *Blue and yellow glass paints*
- *Painting tool or brush*
- *Modelling clay or sticky putty*

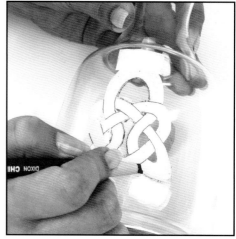

Step 1

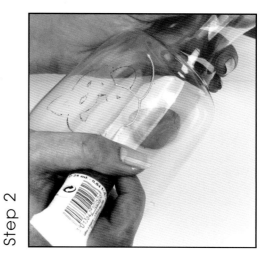

Step 2

Step 1

Trace both Celtic templates and cut them out carefully. Tape the large template to the front of the carafe with small pieces of masking tape. Draw around the edge with a chinagraph pencil, then remove the template.

Step 2

Draw over the chinagraph lines with gold outliner. Also follow the lines which form the intersections of the pattern with gold outliner. Copy the template exactly to get the intersections in the correct places. Leave the outliner to dry completely.

Templates

39

Step 3A

Mix a good supply of a shade of green that you're happy with. Separate part of this and add a touch of red to darken the green. Alternatively, you could use a ready-made green and add a little black paint to get a darker shade.

Step 3B

Support the carafe on its side, using modelling clay or sticky putty to keep it in position. Apply a little dark green paint to the intersection of one section. Fill the rest of the section with light green paint and blend the two together.

Step 4

Paint all the sections of the carafe in the same way. Leave the carafe to dry in a horizontal position to prevent the paint from running.

Step 5

Tape the small Celtic motif to the inside of the glass. Use the gold outliner to draw a line around the outline, and leave it to dry.

Step 6

Paint the motif on the glass in the same way that you painted the motif on the carafe, using a small amount of dark green paint at the intersecting points, and paler green for the main parts of each section. Leave to dry.

Step 3A

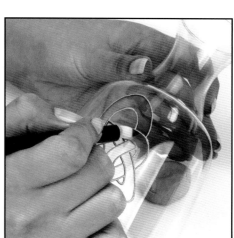

Step 3B

Salad Bowl & Pitcher

YOU WILL NEED:
- *Tracing paper*
- *Soft pencil*
- *Straight-sided glass bowl*
- *Pitcher/jug*
- *Scissors*
- *Masking tape*
- *Glass paints – colours of your choice*
- *Painting tool or brush*
- *Silver outliner pen*

Step 1

Trace the flower template from page 42. Repeat enough times to fit around the edge of your bowl. Roughly cut out these templates and use masking tape to hold them in position all around the bowl.

Step 2

Support the bowl on its side so that you will be painting the flowers horizontally. Position one flower on top. Paint this first flower violet. Leave it to dry before turning the bowl to paint the next flower blue. Again, leave this to dry before turning the bowl to paint the next flower. Paint this one a mixture of violet and blue blended together.

Step 3

Continue painting the flowers, alternating the colours between violet, blue and violet/blue mixed. When the final flower is dry, stand the dish on its base. Use a silver outliner pen to add tiny dots to the centre of each flower. Remove the tracings from inside the bowl.

Step 1

Step 2

Step 3

Salad Bowl & Pitcher (continued)

Step 4

To paint the pitcher, tape a single flower template inside, in the position you want it. Paint over the flower in your favourite colour. When the flower is dry, add silver dots in the centre to match the bowl.

Template

Art Deco Door Panel

YOU WILL NEED:
- *Tracing paper*
- *Soft pencil*
- *Masking tape*
- *Black outliner pen*
- *Glass paints – colours of your choice*
- *Painting tool or brush*

Step 1

Trace the Art Deco design from page 59. You may need to enlarge the template on a photocopier to fit the door panel you intend to paint. When the template is the correct size, trace it on to tracing paper. If at all possible, remove the panel to paint it in a horizontal position.

Step 2

Tape the template behind the glass panel. Draw along each of the outlines with black outliner. Try to use long, flowing movements for each of the lines, keeping each line approximately the same thickness. Leave overnight to ensure the outline is completely dry.

Step 3

Paint the trunk of the tree first, as it is the central part of the design. If you are painting the panel in position, you may find that you have to keep removing paint that has sunk to the bottom of the section, and reapplying paint at the top of the section, to ensure an even colour all the way down. When the trunk is dry, begin to paint the blue of the sky, starting in the centre.

Step 1

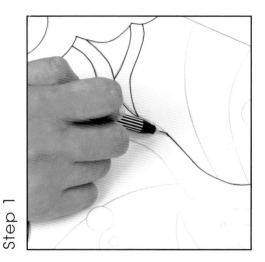

Step 2

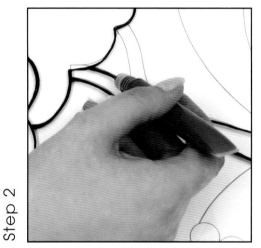

Step 3

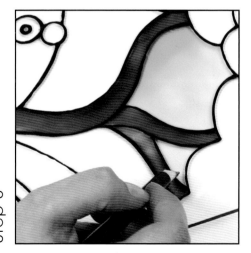

Art Deco Door Panel (continued)

Step 4

Paint each of the dark green sections of the tree's foliage. Allow these to dry, then paint the pale green sections. At the same time, paint the pale green undergrowth sections. Let these dry completely.

Step 5

Paint the large yellow areas at each side of the tree trunk. When these are dry, paint the orange sections alongside.

Step 6

Finally, paint in the brightly-coloured flowers. Start at the centre of each one and fill in the outer petals afterwards.

Step 4

Step 5

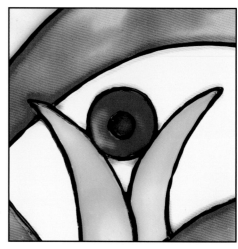

Step 6

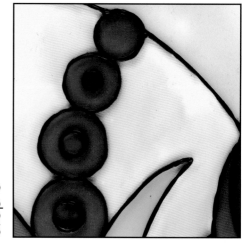

Leaded Vase

YOU WILL NEED:

- *Straight-sided glass vase*
- *Lead stripping (6 mm wide)*
- *Craft knife/scissors*
- *Glass paints – colours of your choice*
- *Boning peg*
- *Painting tool or brush*
- *Kitchen towel*

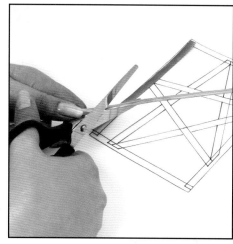

Step 1

Step 1

Lead stripping can be bought from most craft stores, and should have its own instructions for use. The type used in this project has a self-adhesive back, and should be used with a boning peg to help it adhere to the glassware. Use scissors or a craft knife to cut the strips to the correct length for the project.

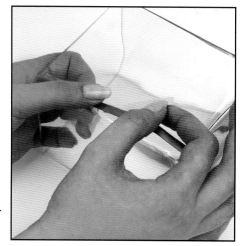

Step 2A

Step 2A

Refer to the template on page 60 to stick the lead stripping in an asymmetric star shape, on the front of the vase. Cut the strips to the correct length, leaving the ends 3 mm inside the edges of the glass.

Step 2B

Fix the strips firmly in place using a boning peg, and following the manufacturer's instructions.

Step 2B

Step 3

Fasten a piece of lead stripping down each outside edge of the front panel, again leaving the strips 3 mm short at the top and bottom. Stick a strip of leading right around the top of the vase, overlapping the edges at the back. Repeat at the bottom of the vase. Check all around to ensure that the edges are hidden and all strips are stuck firmly.

Step 4

Lie the vase on its back with the leaded side facing upwards. Paint the centre section of the star. Use the pointed end of your painting tool to remove circles of paint to reveal the glass underneath. Wipe the excess paint off the tool on to kitchen towel.

Step 5

Paint each point of the star, one by one. Before painting the next point, use your painting tool or the end of a brush to remove circles of paint. Wipe the tool or brush clean on kitchen towel, then move on to paint the next point.

Step 6

Paint one section of the background area using blue paint. Use the pointed end of your painting tool or brush to remove waves of paint, wiping the tool or brush clean each time. Allow the first section to dry and repeat with each of the other background sections.

Step 4

Step 5

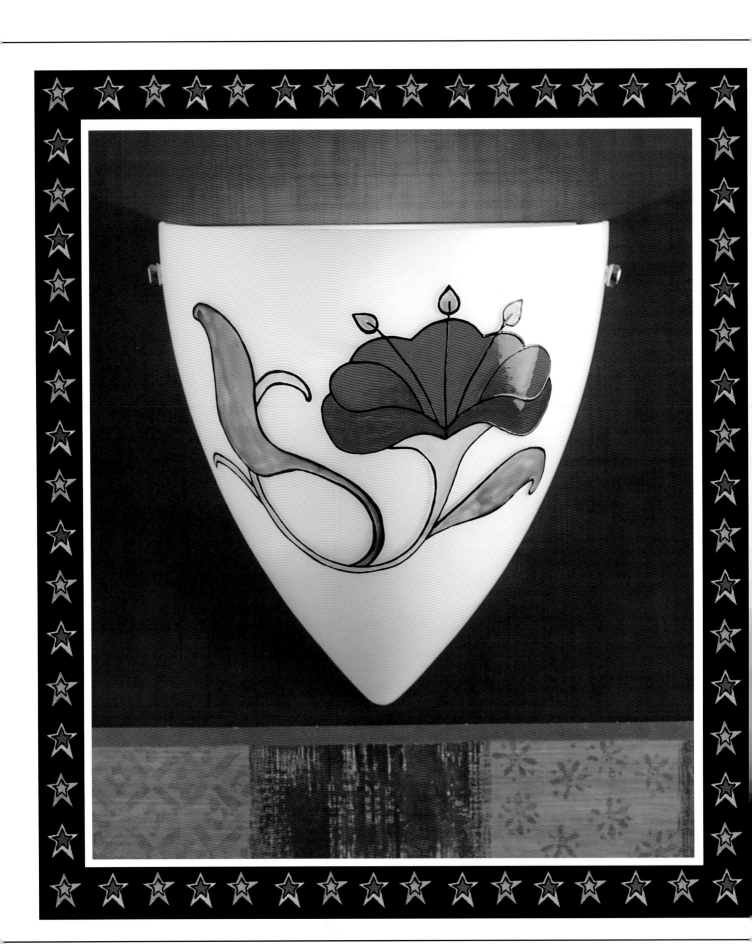

Wall Light

YOU WILL NEED:
- *Tracing paper*
- *Soft pencil and a harder pencil*
- *Scissors*
- *Masking tape*
- *Wall light*
- *Black outliner pen*
- *Glass paints – colours of your choice*
- *Painting tool or brush*

Step 1

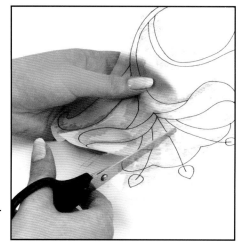

Step 2

Step 3

Step 1

Trace the template from page 55 on to ordinary paper. Use a photocopier to enlarge it or reduce it to the size you need for your wall light, then trace it on to tracing paper.

Step 2

Draw over the design on the reverse using a very soft pencil. Roughly cut out the template.

Step 3

Make cuts in the template to allow you to fit it around the curve of the light. Tape it in place, then draw over the lines with a sharp, hard pencil to transfer the design on to the glass. Remove the template.

Step 4

Carefully draw all the lines of the design using black outliner. Always try to work from the top downwards, to avoid smudging the lines. Leave the outline to dry, overnight if possible.

Step 5

Paint the main flower part of the design, using red for the petals. Start from the centre petal and work outwards. Add depth to the base of some petals by applying a darker shade at the bottom, and a lighter colour at the top. Blend these colours together, and leave to dry.

Step 6

Paint the stamens orange. Turn the light, supporting it so that you can paint the left side in a flat position. Paint the different shades of green, blending them together. Leave this to dry.

Step 7

Turn the light on to its other side so that you can paint the remaining green sections in a flat position. Leave these to dry before fixing the light to the wall.

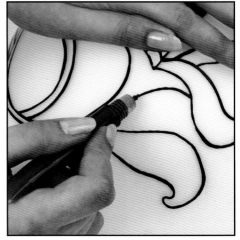

Step 4

Step 5

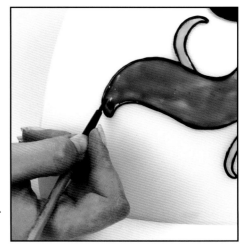

Step 6

Christmas Baubles

YOU WILL NEED:
- Tracing paper
- Soft pencil
- Scissors
- Two-part clear plastic baubles
- Black outliner pen
- Glass paints – colours of your choice
- Painting tool or brush

Step 1

Trace the Christmas templates from page 60 onto tracing paper. Cut them out roughly and make slits in the sides so that the template will fit inside the concave shape of the bauble. Separate the two bauble halves and tape the template inside one.

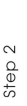

Step 2

Draw around the shapes with black outliner, carefully supporting the underneath of your bauble with your hand. When the outliner is dry, paint the green of the Christmas tree. Move the bauble to keep the painted area horizontal, to prevent the paint from accumulating in one area.

Step 3

When the paint is dry, continue painting in the central areas of the other designs. Leave them to dry, then reassemble the parts of the baubles before hanging them.

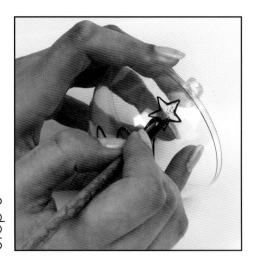

NOTE: If you cannot buy two-part baubles, cut out each template carefully and tape each to the front of a bauble. Draw around the designs with a chinagraph pencil before going over these lines with outliner.

Templates

TEA LIGHT HOLDER PAGE 24-25

NURSERY MOBILE PAGE 20-21

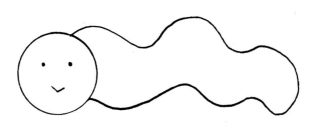

KEY FOBS PAGE 18-19

ART DECO DOOR PANEL 44-47

Templates

LEADED VASE PAGE 48-51

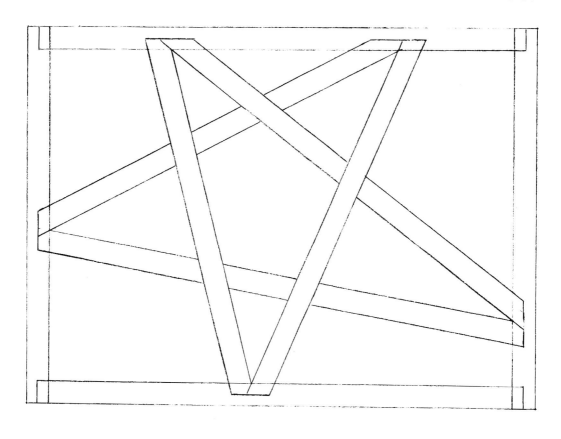

CHRISTMAS BAUBLES 56-57

Templates

BUTTERFLY CARDS PAGE 22-23

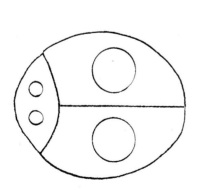

KEY FOBS PAGE 18-19

Templates

ANNIVERSARY BOWL PAGE 33-35

Templates

MIRROR TILE PAGE 30

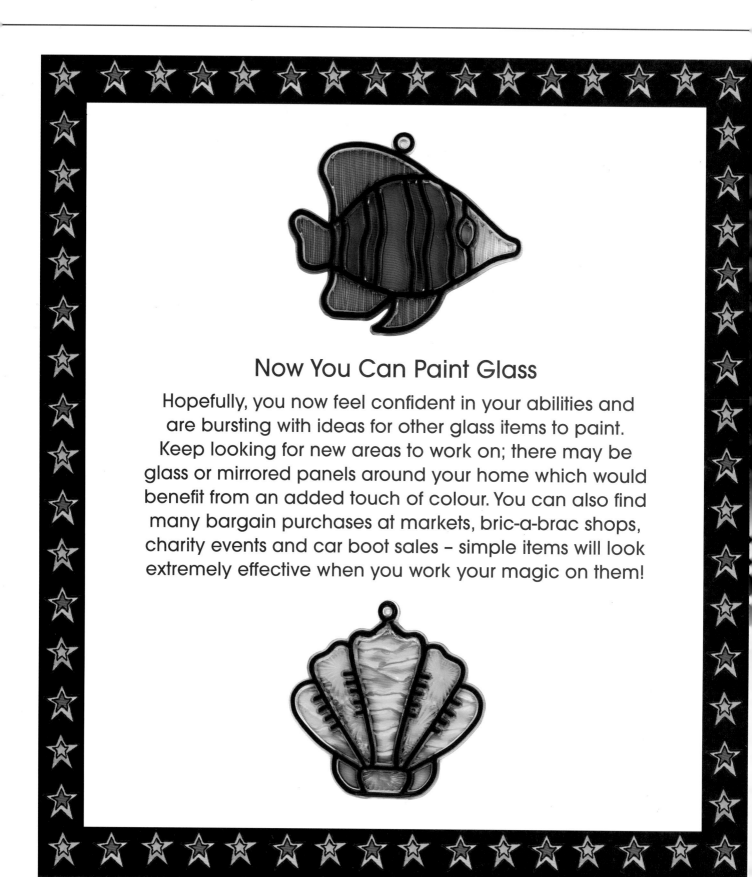

Now You Can Paint Glass

Hopefully, you now feel confident in your abilities and are bursting with ideas for other glass items to paint. Keep looking for new areas to work on; there may be glass or mirrored panels around your home which would benefit from an added touch of colour. You can also find many bargain purchases at markets, bric-a-brac shops, charity events and car boot sales – simple items will look extremely effective when you work your magic on them!

This Walker book belongs to:

_____

_____

_____

First published 2014 by Walker Books Ltd, 87 Vauxhall Walk,

This edition published 2015

10 9 8 7 6 5 4 3 2 1

Text © 2014 William Bee   Illustrations © 2014 Kate Hindley

The right of William Bee and Kate Hindley to be identified as author and
respectively of this work has been asserted by them in accordance with the
and Patents Act 1988

London SE11 5HJ

illustrator
Copyright, Designs

This book has been typeset in Aunt Mildred

Printed in China

British Library Cataloguing in Publication Data:
a catalogue record for this book is available from the British Library

ISBN 978-1-4063-6092-9

www.walker.co.uk

OINKINGHAM TV

WITH SPECIAL THANKS TO
AUDREY, OUR ART DIRECTOR,
AND OUR EDITORS, MARIA
AND MANDY.

WORST IN SHOW

written by
William Bee

illustrated by
Kate Hindley

WALKER BOOKS
AND SUBSIDIARIES

LONDON • BOSTON • SYDNEY • AUCKLAND

This
is Albert.

And this is Albert's pet monster – Sidney.

Albert thinks Sidney is the best
pet monster in the world.

And today, Albert is going to prove it.
Albert is entering
Sidney in ...

TELEVISION
THEATRE

NO
LITTERING

There are five rounds in
THE BEST PET MONSTER IN THE WORLD!
competition and the pet monster
who receives the most points
overall – wins.

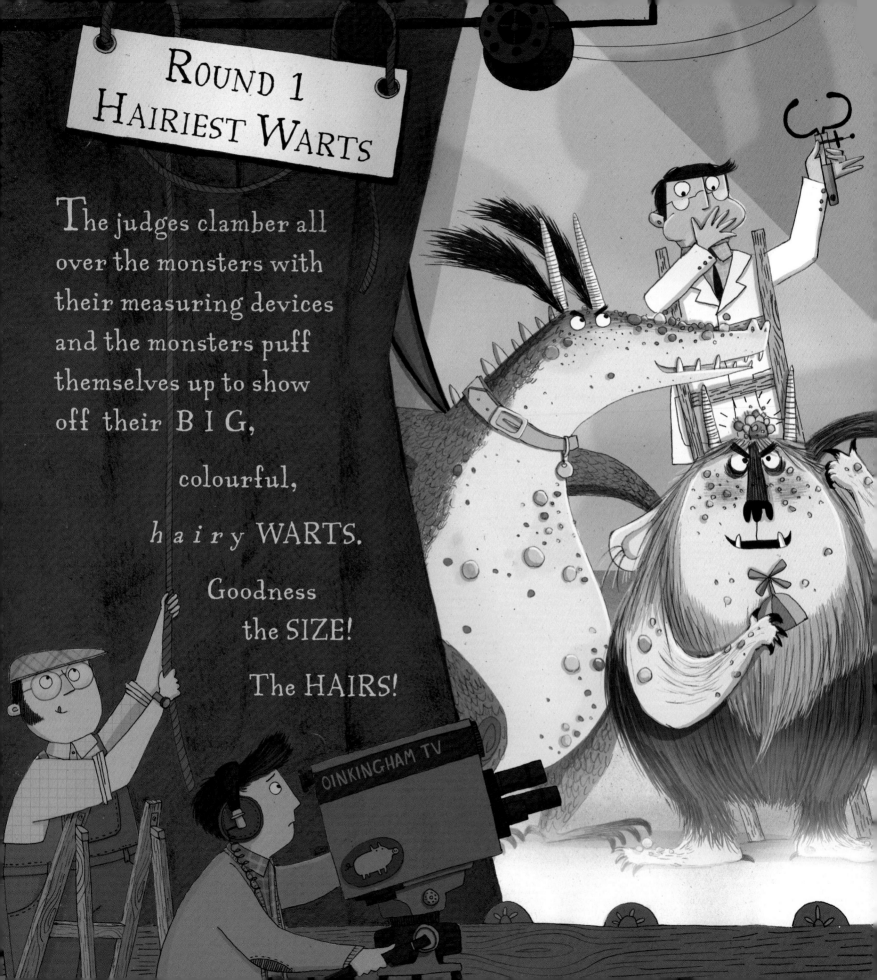

ROUND 1
HAIRIEST WARTS

The judges clamber all over the monsters with their measuring devices and the monsters puff themselves up to show off their B I G,

colourful,

h a i r y WARTS.

Goodness the SIZE!

The HAIRS!

The JUDGES!
One faints and another
comes out in a rash...

Sidney has done his best.

But Sidney, who has a bath every other day
with lots of soap and bubbles hasn't got any warts —
just a few freckles...

GOODNESS
the EMBARRASSMENT!
thinks Albert.

Still, only round one — and who wants a big, HAIRY,
WARTY pet monster anyway?

ROUND 2
HIGHEST HOVER

Everybody has moved outside to see how high the monsters can hover. The judges use hot air balloons and very long tape measures to measure the monsters' hovering height. Goodness the HEIGHT!

The WIND!

50 M

30 M

7

THE BEST
IN TH
COMP

The JUDGES!
One faints and another
floats away in her
untethered balloon...

Sidney has done his best.

But Sidney is scared of heights.
So Sidney hovers very near the ground, so near the ground
in fact that his feet are still touching it...

0 CM

GOODNESS
the EMBARRASSMENT!
thinks Albert.

Still, only round two — and who wants a pet monster
hovering around all day, BUMPING into things anyway?

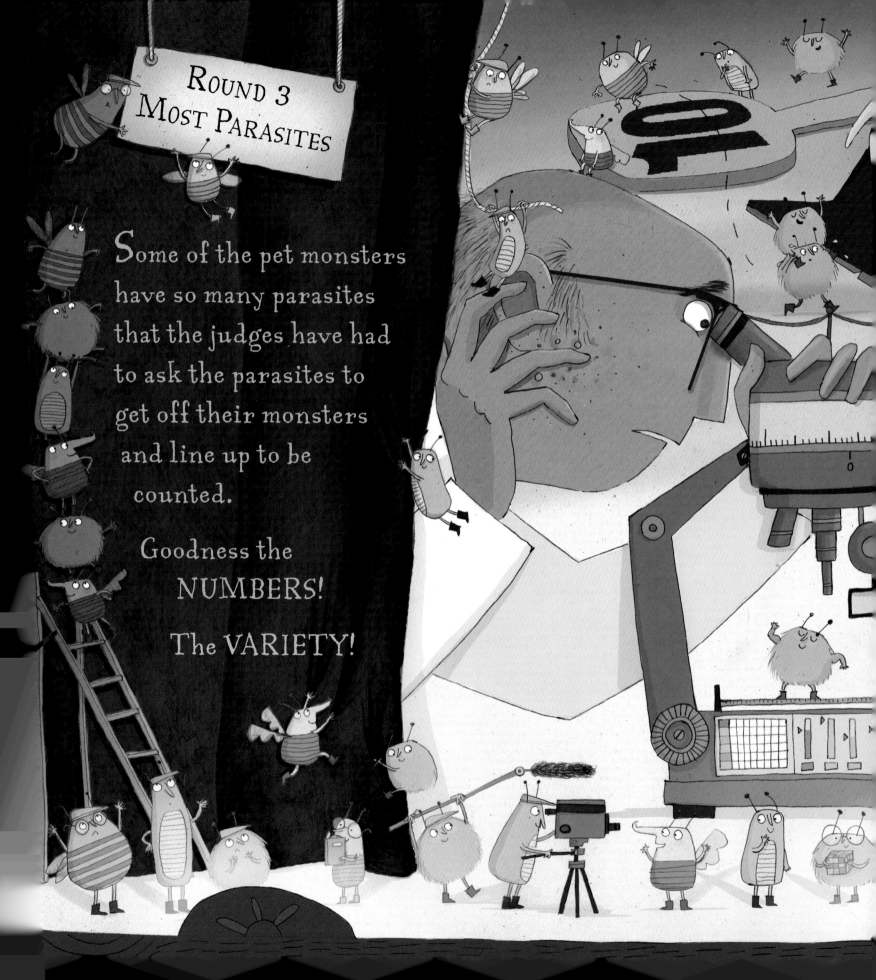

ROUND 3
MOST PARASITES

Some of the pet monsters have so many parasites that the judges have had to ask the parasites to get off their monsters and line up to be counted.

Goodness the NUMBERS!

The VARIETY!

The JUDGES!
One faints and another
starts scratching
frantically!

Sidney has done his best.

But Sidney only has two parasites — Stan and Ollie.
And as Stan and Ollie are just staying for a few days ...
they are really holidaymakers rather than parasites.

GOODNESS
the EMBARRASSMENT!
thinks Albert.

Still, only round three — and who wants a
pet monster with hundreds of parasites hanging about
causing all sorts of MISCHIEF anyway?

ROUND 4
SMELLIEST FART

The monsters all
position themselves,
and on the count of
three ... they all
FART!

Goodness the
SMELL!

The NOISE!

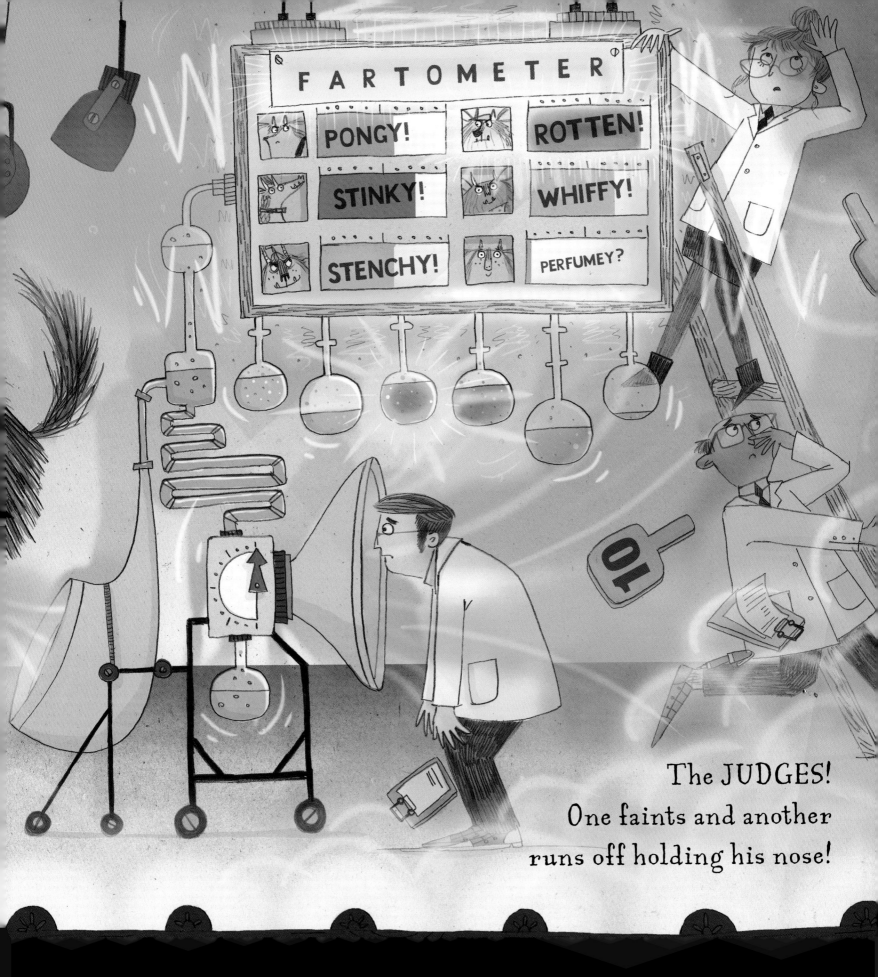

The JUDGES!
One faints and another
runs off holding his nose!

Sidney has done his best.

But a diet of iced biscuits and fairy cakes
means barely a whiff —
and a sugary whiff at that...

SILENCE
THE WINGS

GOODNESS
the EMBARRASSMENT!
thinks Albert.

FART BUSTER
2000

Still, only round four — and who wants a big SMELLY
pet monster anyway?

It's the final round.

ROUND 5
HOTTEST BREATH

There is chaos onstage!
The monsters take in great
big gulps of air and breathe
out great big bellows of fire!
One of the TV cameras
catches alight and so
do the curtains!
    Goodness
        the HEAT!

The SMOKE!

The JUDGES!
One faints and another
runs away holding
her hot bottom!

Sidney has done his best.

But he has only been able to warm up a party sausage
that Albert has put on a little fork...

GOODNESS
the EMBARRASSMENT!
thinks Albert, forlornly.

Still, who wants their BOTTOM
set on fire anyway?

After all the day's excitement, at last —
it's time for the prize giving!

Albert and Sidney wait in
eager anticipation as the
dignitaries hand out
the trophies.

HAIRIEST
WARTS

MOST
PARASITES

HIGHEST
HOVER

Best in Show

SMELLIEST FARTS

But as trophy after trophy is presented to the other pet monsters, it becomes apparent to Albert and Sidney that they are not amongst the winners. GOODNESS the EMBARRASSMENT!

But wait!

Albert and Sidney's names are being called out!
Winners after all?

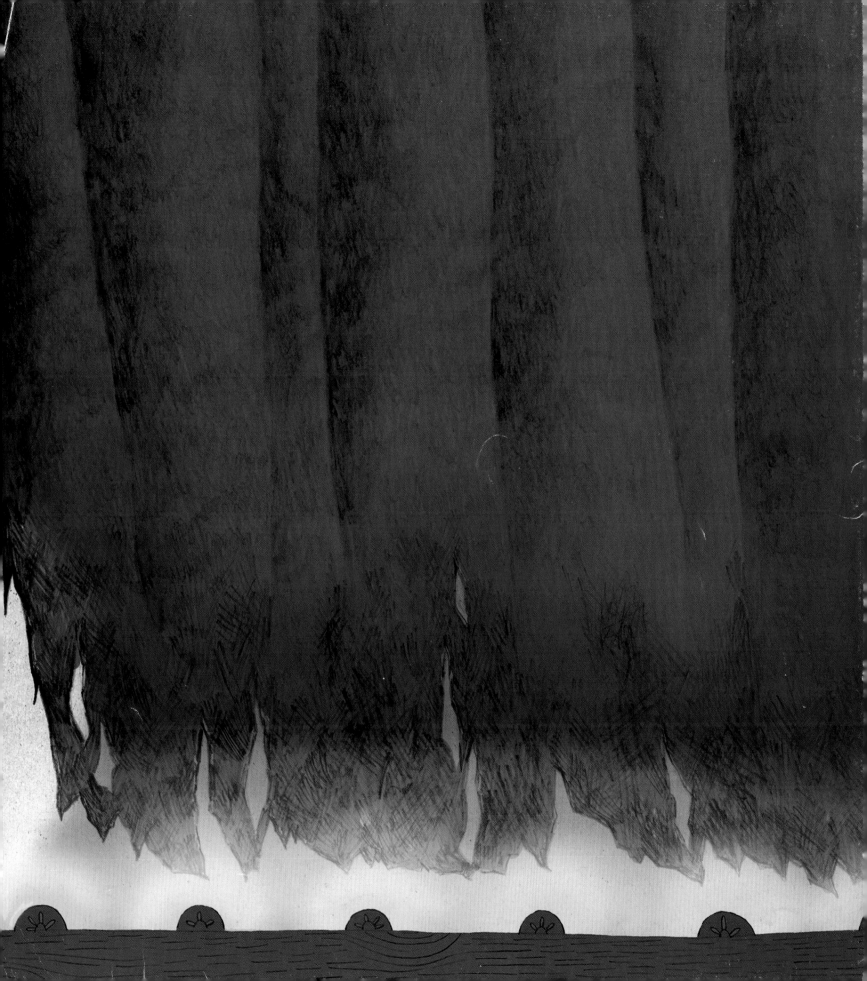

Worst in Show!

GOODNESS the EMBARRASSMENT!
Still, thinks Albert, who wants a big, HAIRY,
HIGH-FLYING, PARASITE-INFESTED,
SMELLY, FLAMMABLE,
pet monster ANYWAY?!

Especially when you can have a
BIG, CUDDLY, LOVABLE...
BEST FRIEND.*

*(Who smells GREAT!)

HOME

Also by William Bee:

and the train goes...

william bee

ISBN: 978-1-4063-4488-2

Migloo's Day

william bee

He's everyone's favourite dog! migloo

ISBN: 978-1-4063-3930-7

and the cars go...

william bee

ISBN: 978-1-4063-5259-7

Also by Kate Hindley:

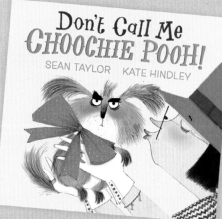

Don't Call Me CHOOCHIE POOH!

SEAN TAYLOR   KATE HINDLEY

ISBN: 978-1-4063-4560-5

Available from all good booksellers

www.walker.co.uk